This book belongs to:

....

How to be a Fairy

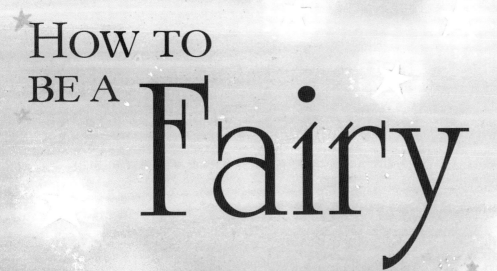

Written by
Nicola Baxter

Illustrated by
Beverlie Manson

ARMADILLO

This edition published in 2007 by Bookmart Ltd

Published by
Armadillo Books
an imprint of
Bookmart Limited
Registered Number 2372865
Trading as Bookmart Limited
Blaby Road Wigston
Leicester LE18 4SE

ISBN 978-1-84322-421-1

10 9 8 7 6 5 4 3

Produced for Bookmart Limited
by Nicola Baxter
PO Box 215 Framingham Earl
Norwich NR14 7UR

Designer: Amanda Hawkes
Production designer: Amy Barton
Editor: Sally Delaney
Assistant editor: Rosalind Knight

Printed in Thailand

Contents

Fairies for Ever

BY FAIRY SELINA

My dear fairy-to-be, welcome to the world of fairies! Did you know that fairies have lived on Earth for millions of years? And they will go on living here as long as new fairies—just like you—keep wanting to learn fairy ways and live the fairy law.

Learning to become a fairy is not difficult, but you will probably find that you never *stop* learning new and fascinating things about us.

Did you know, for example, that there are fairies all over the world?

We live in tropical forests and on freezing icebergs.

We live in air and in water and even underground.

We live in the countryside and in homes, but we are hardly ever seen. Only sometimes, you might just catch sight of one of us out of the corner of your eye.

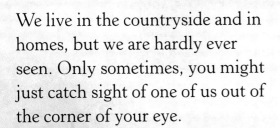

Most of us have wings, but some do not. Most of us are girls, but there are boy fairies, too! And yet, whoever we are and wherever we live, we all follow the fairy law.

So how can you become a fairy? Just read this book to find out!

Your Fairy Name

BY FAIRY BUTTERFLY

Each fairy needs a special name, and it is not a name given to her by someone else. A fairy has to go out and find her own true name when she starts to follow the fairy law. There are several different ways of doing this. Choose whichever you like best.

★ *A Dreamy Name*

Some fairies believe that the best way to find a real fairy name is in a dream. Each morning, when they wake up, they write down everything they can remember about their dreams from the night before. If you do this, keep your notes in a secret notebook, hidden away. It may take days or weeks, but one morning you will find that you have written down a word that is perfect as your fairy name.

★ Nature's Name

Many fairies use this method to find their special names. One day when the breeze is warm and the weather kind, stand outside in a peaceful, pretty spot and close your eyes. Slowly turn around three times, then open your eyes again. Look quietly, and say out loud the first thing you see. It could be a flower, a cloud, a leaf or an insect—or anything. If you are not happy with the result, try again, perhaps in another place, until the name seems right to you.

★ A Lucky Name

Finally, you could try this method. Each night for nine nights, write down twelve fairy names on slips of paper. At the end, you will have 108 slips. Put them in a box, close your eyes, and choose one. That's your fairy name!

Remember… Your fairy name is a secret name. You should really only tell it to other fairies. If someone else finds out about it by accident, it doesn't matter too much, but if you prefer, you can decide to find another name —and keep it secret this time!

The Fairy Law

BY FAIRY ROSEBUD

Real fairies all follow the fairy law. It is perfectly simple and has just three parts.

Young fairies learn the fairy law by heart. It's a good idea to do that yourself.

Look for magic in everything you see and everyone you meet.

Be kind to others and to yourself.

Take care of the wonderful world in which you live.

★ *If you make a mistake...*

We all make mistakes sometimes—even fairies! If you think you have broken the fairy law, here's what you need to do.

1. Think carefully about what you have done. Try to understand why it happened and what you can do to stop it happening again.

2. Put things right as far as you can. If you have hurt someone you love, for example, make sure they know how sorry you are and try to make up for your mistake.

3. Hold your fairy charm and make a special promise to yourself that you will follow the fairy law again.

Fairy Finery

BY FAIRY RAINBOW

When you feel like a fairy and think like a fairy, you want to look like a fairy. I'm here to give you some tips on fairy fashion and magical makeovers. All fairies like to look pretty, but they know that how you feel on the inside is what makes the biggest difference to how you look on the outside.

Fairies use all kinds of beautiful things to make their clothes: petals, leaves, ribbons, bows, cobwebs, moonbeams, even rainbows! Here are some of my best-dressed friends.

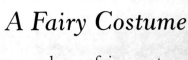

A Fairy Costume

You can buy a fairy costume, but it is more fun to make your own. Here is an easy idea for a special fairy skirt—with no sewing at all!

The skirt would look pretty worn over a swimsuit or a leotard.

All you need to begin is a piece of elastic long enough to go around your waist. Knot the ends together so that it is loose enough to pull on and off easily but tight enough to stay in place.

Now have fun! Simply tuck pretty things under the elastic, knotting them if you like, until you have a fairy skirt. You could use: strips of spare fabric, strings of silk flowers, ribbons, tinsel or party streamers, scarves or anything else you like. The best thing is, your skirt will not look like anyone else's at all.

Fairies love pretty things, and they find them everywhere they look. A dewdrop sparkling on a spider's web can be as beautiful as the loveliest flower. Here are some easy ways to make fairy accessories that any fairy would love to wear or use.

★ *Star Quality*

It takes years of training to learn to catch a falling star to wear in your hair, so why not trace the templates below and use them to cut star shapes from card? You can decorate them with glitter or paints and use them in lots of ways.

Glue a large star to the end of a pot-plant stake or a piece of dowel. Use ribbon, glitter and paints to decorate it and make your own fairy wand!

Glue a star to each end of thread about 10cm long. Hook the thread over your ear for dangly earrings!

Glue small glittery stars to ordinary hair grips for starry fairy hairstyles. (Make sure the glue is dry before you wear them!)

Use your starry hair grips to decorate your shoes and clothes. Just unclip them when you want to.

★ *Daisy Chains*

It's not usually a good idea to pick wild flowers. They look more beautiful left to grow than wilting in a jar. But daisies grow almost everywhere, and it is lovely to sit in the shade on a sunny afternoon and make a daisy-chain bracelet, necklace or crown.

Simply pick a daisy with a long stalk, make a little slit in the stalk with your thumbnail, and thread another daisy stalk through. Repeat this until your chain is as long as you need.

Makeover Magic

BY FAIRY STARLIGHT

Smiling fairies look pretty all the time, but sometimes they want to look a little special for a party or a fairy fiesta. You could try some of our magical makeovers.

★ *Spellbinding Styles*

Whether your hair is long or short, some pretty, glittery clips or bands will look lovely. You could try this twisty-turny style, too.

Simply take small sections of hair and twist them. With short hair, pin the twists in position with pretty clips.

With longer hair, start at the front from a centre parting and twist away from the parting on one side, adding in new sections of hair as you go. Do the same on the other side. Use a hair band to hold the twists in place at the back.

★ Make-up

Fairies prefer a naturally pretty look but, of course, they love to have fun, too. A moonbeam here and a little starshine there is lovely for a party face. You could try a little pearly lip balm and some glitter gel on your cheeks. Never use anything that is not specially made to be put on skin.

After a party, don't forget to remove all your make-up with soap and water or a little baby lotion on cotton wool. Comb any glitter from your hair and get a good night's sleep—it's the best fairy beauty tip of all!

★ Finally ... a Message from the Tooth Fairy

Dear fairies, do remember that a friendly smile makes you look lovelier than any makeover. Take care of your beautiful teeth, for they are a very special part of your fairy charm.

Fairy Feasts

BY FAIRY PEACHTREE

When fairies meet they love to prepare fairy food and drink for each other. Of course, the portions are tiny, but nothing is so delicious as fairy food eaten bite by tiny bite. Try these easy recipes to make a feast for friends, whether they are fairies or not.

Spellbinding Savoury Snacks

Tiny, tasty mouthfuls are easy to make. Make sandwiches with thinly cut bread and your favourite fillings. Then ask an adult to help you cut them into very small triangles (with the crusts removed, of course!) Or you can use little cookie cutters to make them flower-shaped, star-shaped, even fairy-shaped!

More tiny treats can be made using those little cheesy biscuits sometimes called cocktail biscuits.

They are already tasty, so top them with little dabs of yeast extract or savoury spread and sprinkle with grated parmesan cheese, sesame seeds or poppy seeds.

A Feast of Flowers

Here is a pretty salad that is very easy to make but even more delicious if you grow the ingredients yourself. All fairies have green fingers. It's time to show off yours!

You will need:
a bag of compost
two large plant pots
a packet of seeds for
        mixed salad leaves
a packet of nasturtium seeds

1. Fill the pots with compost to about 5cm from the top of the pot. If you put a few stones or pieces of broken pot in first, the compost won't fall out of the holes in the bottom.

2. Plant each packet of seeds (you may not need all that you have) in its own pot, following the instructions on the packet.

3. Keep your pots in a light place indoors or in the garden in the summer. Water them when the compost is dry and take care of them as little plants appear and grow. In a few weeks, you will have salad leaves that are large enough to cut or pick, and flowers on your nasturtiums.

4. Pick leaves and flowers, wash them carefully, then scatter them in a bowl. Serve with your favourite salad dressing.

★ *Fairy Cakes*

Make sure you have an adult with you all the time to help with the oven and mixing.

You will need:
125g soft butter or margarine
125g caster sugar
2 eggs
125g self-raising flour
5ml (1tsp) baking powder
bun or mini-muffin paper cases

1. Preheat the oven to 190°C/375°F/Gas 5.

2. Put all the ingredients in a bowl and mix together with a wooden spoon or hand-mixer to make a smooth mixture.

3. Put the paper cases in bun or mini-muffin tins. Use a teaspoon to fill each about a third full of mixture.

4. Bake until golden brown. How long this takes will depend on how big your cases are— between 5 and 20 minutes.

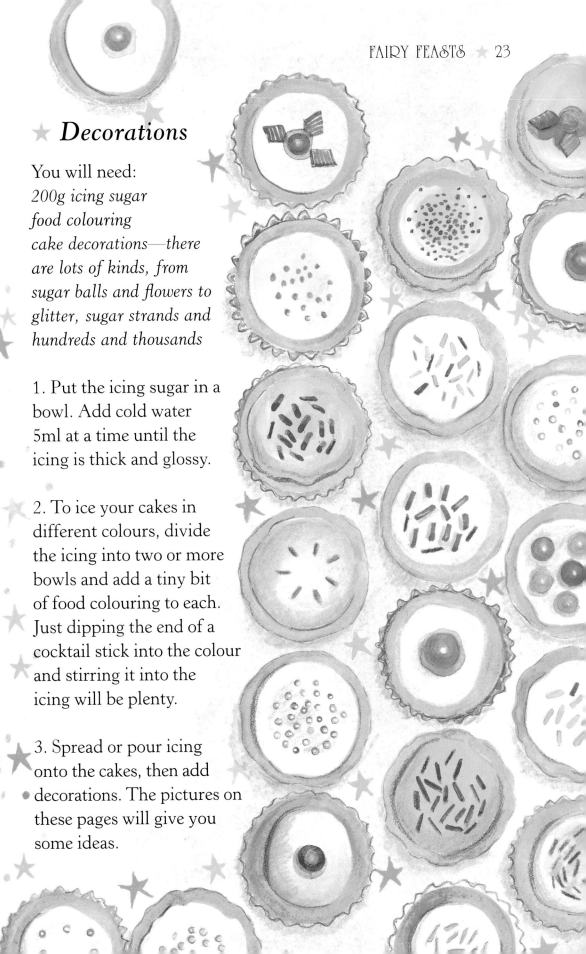

★ *Decorations*

You will need:
200g icing sugar
food colouring
cake decorations—there
are lots of kinds, from
sugar balls and flowers to
glitter, sugar strands and
hundreds and thousands

1. Put the icing sugar in a bowl. Add cold water 5ml at a time until the icing is thick and glossy.

2. To ice your cakes in different colours, divide the icing into two or more bowls and add a tiny bit of food colouring to each. Just dipping the end of a cocktail stick into the colour and stirring it into the icing will be plenty.

3. Spread or pour icing onto the cakes, then add decorations. The pictures on these pages will give you some ideas.

Super Spells

BY FAIRY FLUELLA

Some fairies spend their whole lives studying spelling, but don't worry! The basics are easy to learn, and you can start straight away. The important thing is to really mean the spell and not to skimp on the number of times you say it.

A Spell for Sweet Dreams

You need to be in bed and ready for sleep before you begin. Start by thinking about the day that is ending. If things have happened that are worrying you, decide what you can do about them tomorrow and put them to one side for tonight.

Then lie very still and say very softly

The day is done,
The night is come,
May sweet sleep
Bring sweeter dreams
To carry me to morning.

You need to say this once for every year of your age. Don't worry if you fall asleep in the middle. It just means that you're a powerful spellmaker!

★ A Spell for Luck

This is useful before a test or a performance, but it helps if you have practised really carefully what you have to do as well.

You need to think about all the people you have ever helped or who wish you well. Then say:

What I have given,
I call to my aid.
Warm wishes will help me.
I'll not be afraid.
Whatever is looked for,
  I can show.
Whatever is needed, I can do.

If you like, you can say this spell three times while holding a lucky object, such as your fairy charm. After that, touching or looking at the object will refresh the spell.

★ A Spell for Beauty

There is no such thing as an ugly fairy! By deciding to become a fairy, you have decided to be beautiful, so a spell is hardly necessary, but just in case…

Say this silently to yourself at any time. Remember that you are a beautiful part of a beautiful world.

Like the oak, I am strong.
Like the rose, I am fair.
Like a bird, my thoughts fly
And dance in the air.
Hovering between the earth and
  the sky,
A fairy is free, and so am I.

★ A Spell for Good Weather

This spell is tricky for one very good reason. It is a fairy rule that you must never use magic that could hurt someone else. If you are holding a picnic or going to a sports event, you may well want a spell for a fine day, but suppose a farmer down the road is desperate for rain? You can see that magic isn't always simple. This spell won't do anyone else any harm, but you may be wise to plan what you will do if it is wet!

Hold your fairy charm in your left hand and face the direction of the sun by day or the moon by night.

If all is fine,
Let it be fine
On the [add the date] of [month].

Say the spell three times each day, finishing on the morning of the day when you need good weather.

★ For One You Love

Whisper this seven times to take care of someone you love.

May [name] be safe this day.
May [name] be happy this day.
May [name] do well this day,
And sometimes think of me.

Touch your fairy charm as you whisper this.

★ *Your Own Spells*

It isn't hard to create your own spells if you remember some simple rules.

1. Spells are called spells because they spell out, or make clear, something you are feeling or wishing. Make sure you have worked out exactly what you want and state it clearly in your spell.

2. A spell will never work if it harms someone else.

3. A spell doesn't need to rhyme, but you should say it more than once. With practice, you will know how many times to do this.

4. A spell can be more powerful if you hold an object that is important to you. Your fairy charm is always useful for this.

5. Relax! Fairies know that magic works best when you don't try too hard!

Fairy Treasures

BY FAIRY SEASPRAY

Many fairies have a secret place where they keep the things that are most precious to them— perhaps a beautiful shell, a pretty pebble, a tiny feather, or a lovely autumn leaf. Now that you have begun to become a fairy, you might like to make your own collection. You could add delicate necklaces and bracelets, hair decorations, fairy stickers, and, of course, your special fairy charm.

A Fairy Treasure Chest

You will need:
a shoe box
coloured paper
glue
paints and crayons
glitter
stick-on jewels or sequins
scissors
cardboard egg boxes

Simply cover your box with pretty paper and then decorate it in your own special fairy style. Cut up egg boxes to fit inside, so that you have lots of little compartments to keep tiny fairy treasures safe.

The Best Fairy Treasures of All

You know, when I asked some fairy friends what their most precious treasures were, their answers surprised me, but I think they were right, don't you?

"A kind heart is the most precious thing of all."

"What do I treasure most? A smile from a friend!"

"When you look at the world with fairy eyes, you see treasures everywhere!"